CLASSICAL

SHOWTUNES

CLASSIC HITS

A Love Before Time

From 'Crouching Tiger, Hidden Dragon'

Music by Tan Dun

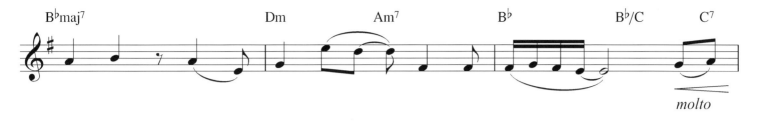

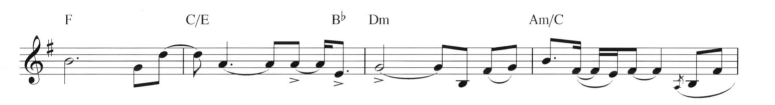

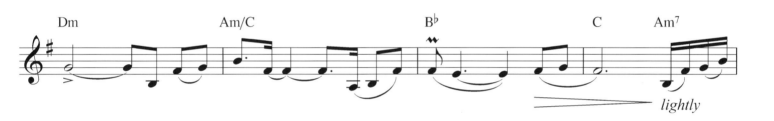

All Love Can Be

From 'A Beautiful Mind'

Words by Will Jennings
Music by James Horner

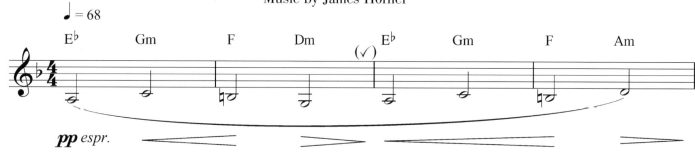

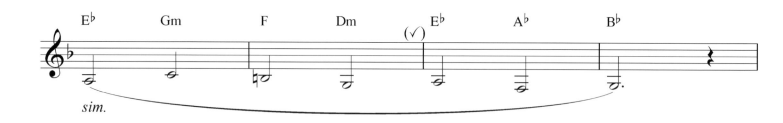

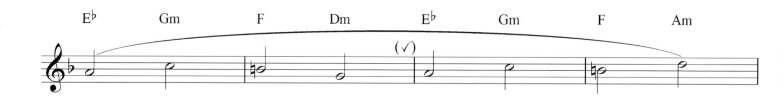

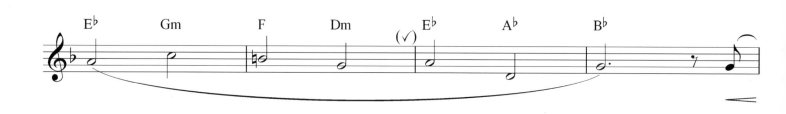

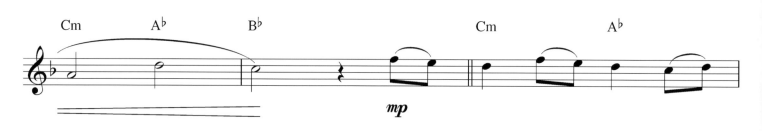

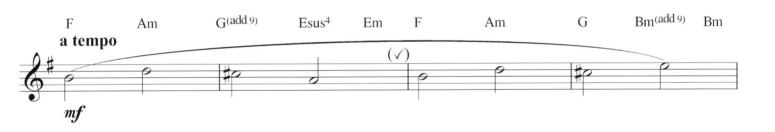

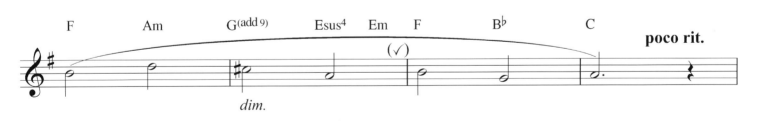

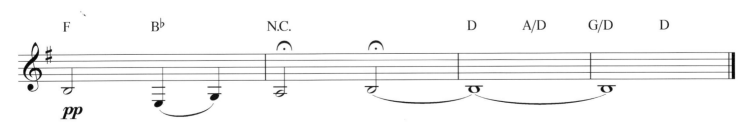

A Whole New World

From 'Aladdin'

Music by Alan Menken
Words by Tim Rice

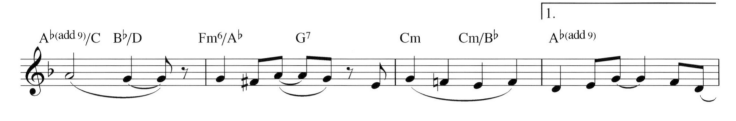

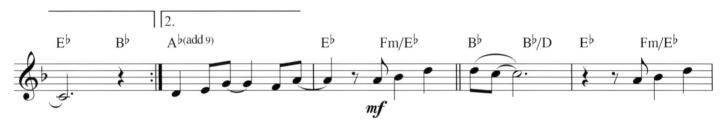

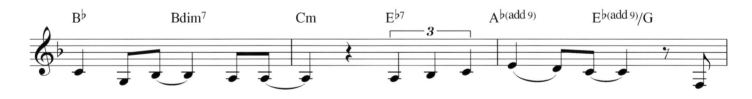

The Godfather
(Love Theme)

Music by Nino Rota

Goldfinger

(Theme)

Words by Leslie Bricusse & Anthony Newley
Music by John Barry

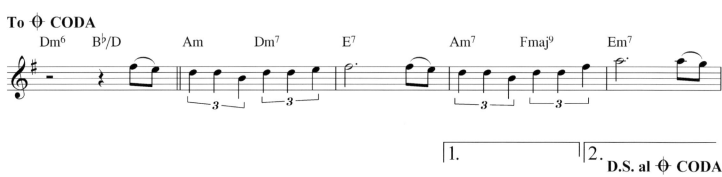

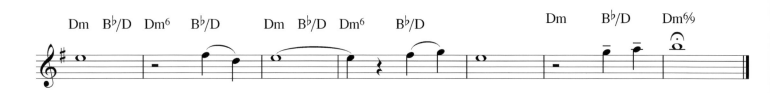

10

I Will Always Love You

From 'The Bodyguard'

Words & Music by Dolly Parton

Mission: Impossible
(Theme)

Music by Lalo Schifrin

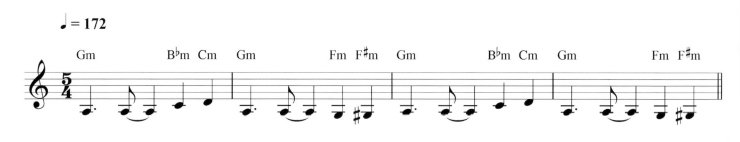

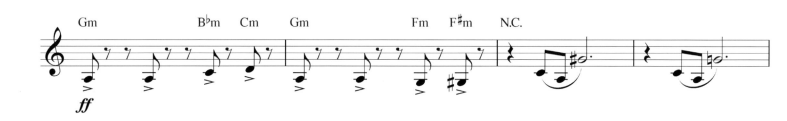

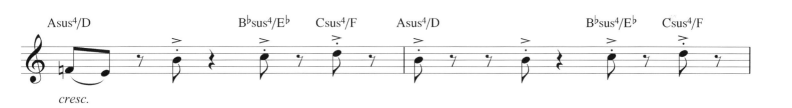

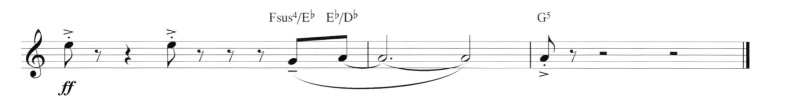

My Heart Will Go On
Love Theme from 'Titanic'

Words by Will Jennings
Music by James Horner

Passage Of Time
From the Miramax Motion Picture 'Chocolat'

Music by Rachel Portman

16

Moon River

From 'Breakfast At Tiffany's'

Words by Johnny Mercer
Music by Henry Mancini

Don't Know Why

Words & Music by Jesse Harris

Angels

Words & Music by Robbie Williams & Guy Chambers

21

Beautiful

Words & Music by Linda Perry

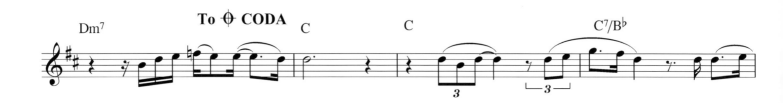

D.S. al ⊕ CODA

⊕ **CODA**

Crazy

Words & Music by Thomas Callaway, Brian Burton,
Gianfranco Reverberi & Gian Piero Reverberi

Don't Look Back In Anger

Words & Music by Noel Gallagher

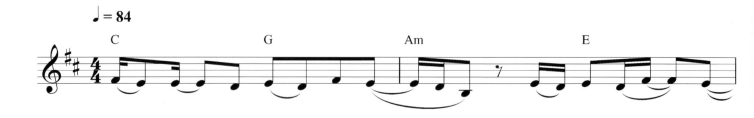

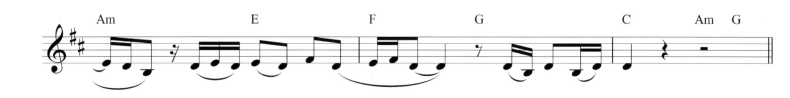

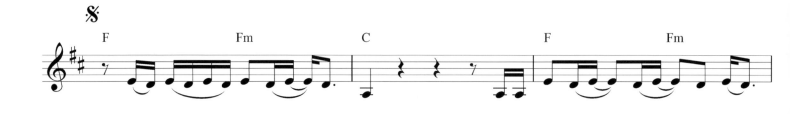

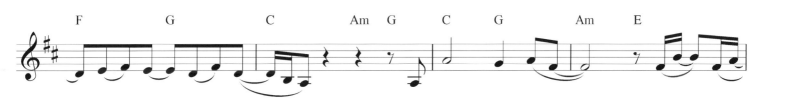

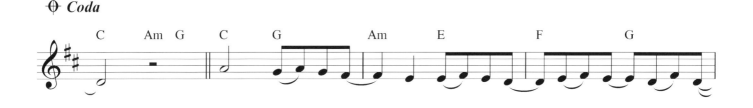

Fields Of Gold

Words & Music by Sting

Put Your Records On

Words & Music by John Beck,
Steven Chrisanthou & Corinne Bailey Rae

Fix You

Words & Music by Coldplay, Guy Berryman,
Chris Martin, Jon Buckland & Will Champion

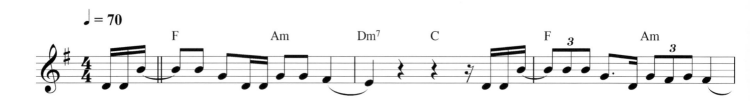

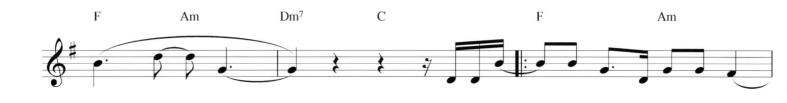

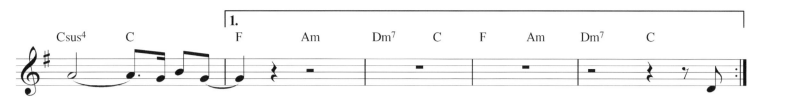

Nothing In My Way

Words & Music by Richard Hughes, James Sanger,
Tim Rice-Oxley & Tom Chaplin

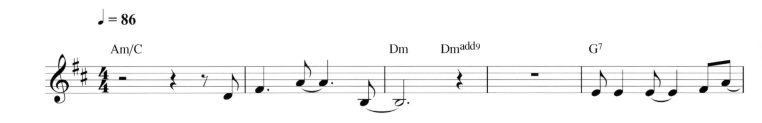

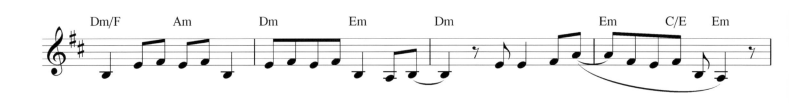

Other Side Of The World

Words & Music by KT Tunstall & Martin Terefe

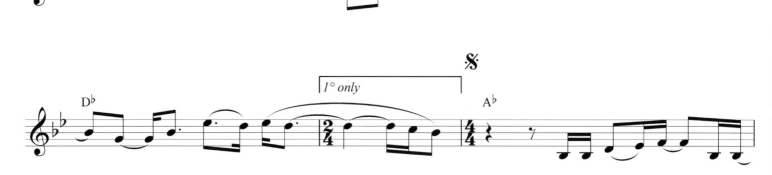

Ain't That A Kick In The Head

Words by Sammy Cahn
Music by Jimmy Van Heusen

Fly Me To The Moon (In Other Words)

Words & Music by Bart Howard

Besame Mucho

Words & Music by Consuelo Velazquez

Don't Get Around Much Anymore

Words by Bob Russell
Music by Duke Ellington

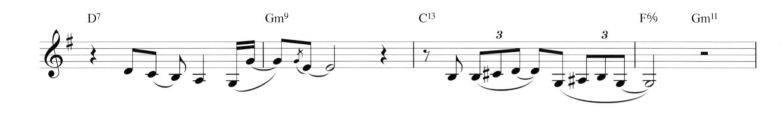

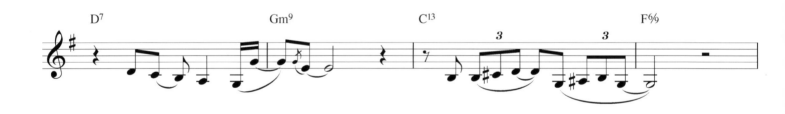

Fever

Words & Music by John Davenport & Eddie Cooley

Moderate jump beat

43

The Girl From Ipanema

(Garota De Ipanema)

Words by Vinicius De Moraes
Music by Antonio Carlos Jobim

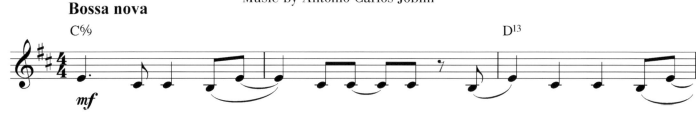

Moonglow

Words & Music by Will Hudson, Eddie De Lange & Irving Mills

Perdido

Words by Ervin Drake & Harry Lenk
Music by Juan Tizol

In A Sentimental Mood

Words & Music by Duke Ellington, Irving Mills & Manny Kurtz

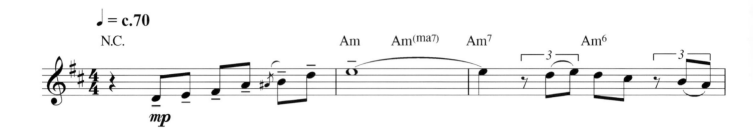

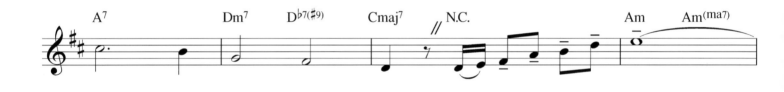

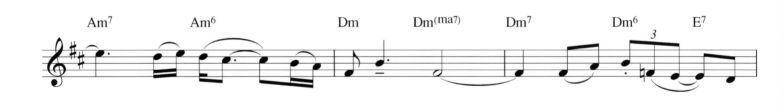

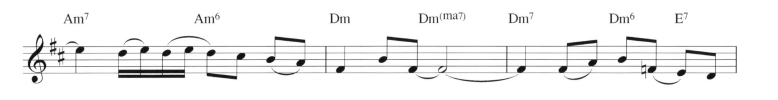

Satin Doll

Words by Johnny Mercer
Music by Duke Ellington & Billy Strayhorn

Barcarolle

From 'The Tales Of Hoffmann'

Music by Jacques Offenbach

Ave Maria

Music by Franz Schubert

Clair de Lune

Music by Claude Debussy

Entr'acte
From 'Rosamunde'

Music by Franz Schubert

Gymnopédie No.1

Music by Erik Satie

Largo
From 'Xerxes'

Music by George Frideric Handel

Jesu, Joy Of Man's Desiring

Music by Johann Sebastian Bach

O For The Wings Of A Dove

Music by Felix Mendelssohn

Polovtsian Dance No.17

From 'Prince Igor'

Music by Alexander Borodin

Promenade
From 'Pictures At An Exhibition'

Music by Modest Mussorgsky

Any Dream Will Do

From 'Joseph And The Amazing Technicolor® Dreamcoat'

Music by Andrew Lloyd Webber
Lyrics by Tim Rice

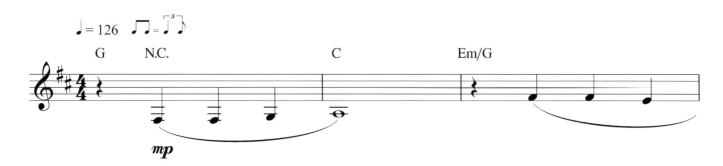

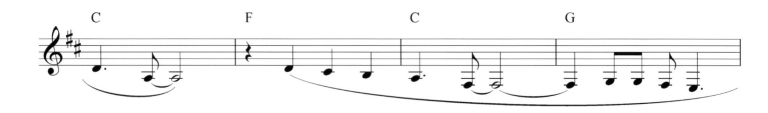

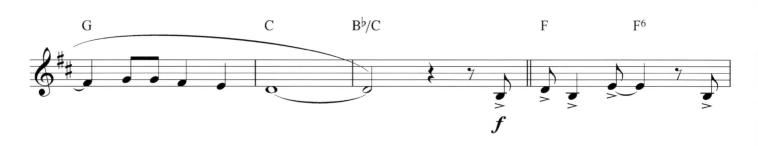

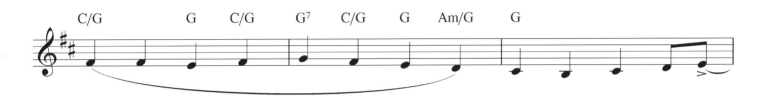

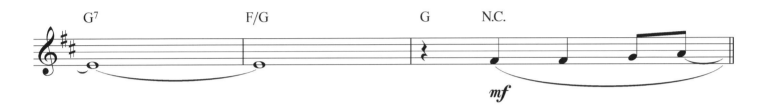

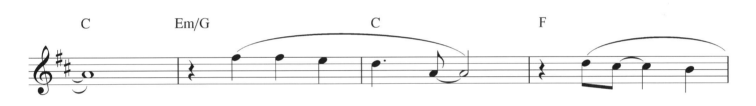

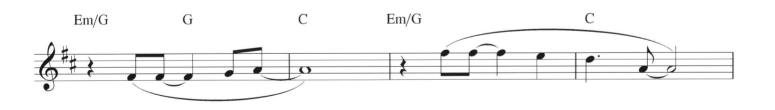

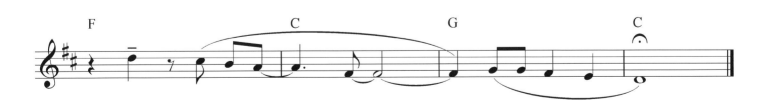

Can You Feel The Love Tonight
From 'The Lion King'

Words by Tim Rice
Music by Elton John

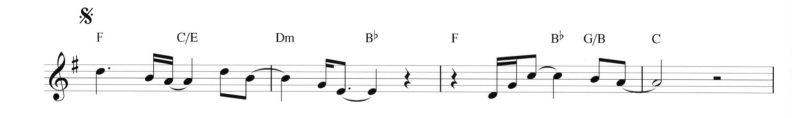

To Coda ⊕

D.S. al Coda

⊕ *Coda*

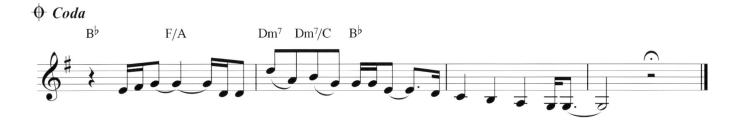

I Dreamed A Dream

From 'Les Misérables'

Music by Claude-Michel Schönberg
Original Lyrics by Alain Boublil & Jean-Marc Natel
English Lyrics by Herbert Kretzmer

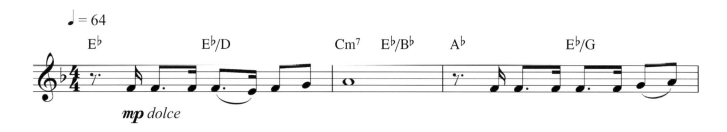

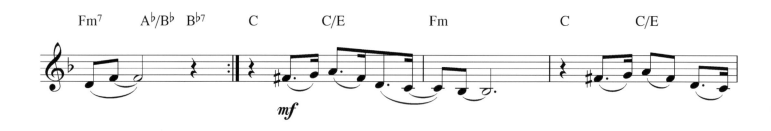

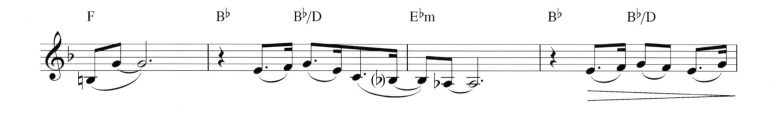

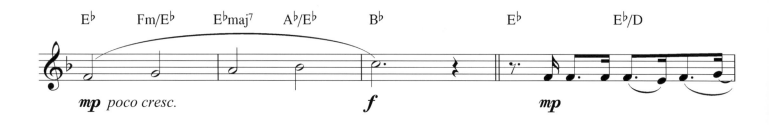

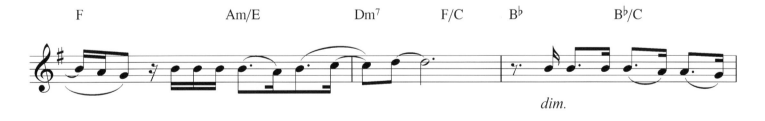

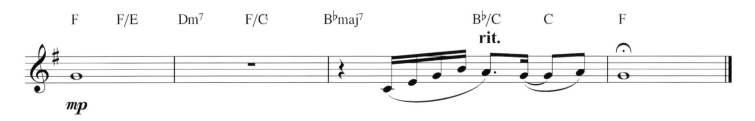

If I Were A Rich Man

From 'Fiddler On The Roof'

Words by Sheldon Harnick
Music by Jerry Bock

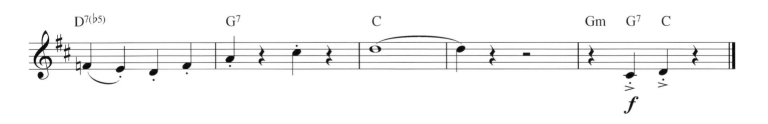

71

Don't Cry For Me Argentina

From 'Evita'

Music by Andrew Lloyd Webber
Lyrics by Tim Rice

Mamma Mia
From 'Mamma Mia'

Words & Music by Benny Andersson, Stig Anderson & Björn Ulvaeus

Memory
From 'Cats'

Music by Andrew Lloyd Webber
Text by Trevor Nunn after T.S. Eliot

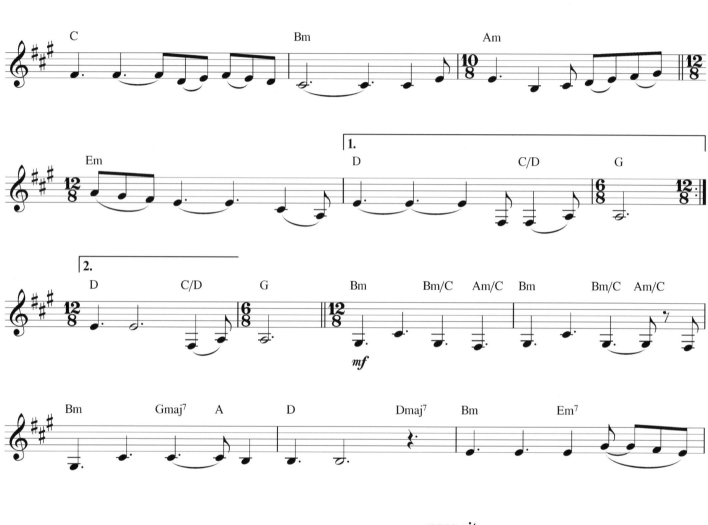

The Music Of The Night

From 'The Phantom Of The Opera'

Music by Andrew Lloyd Webber
Lyrics by Charles Hart

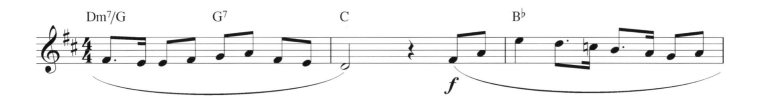

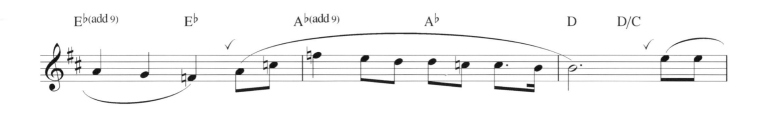

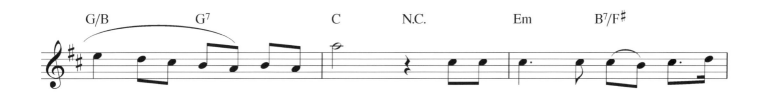

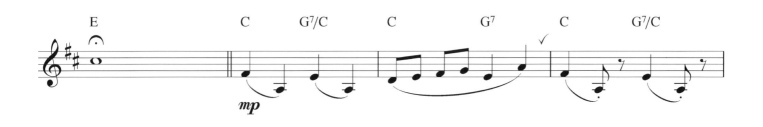

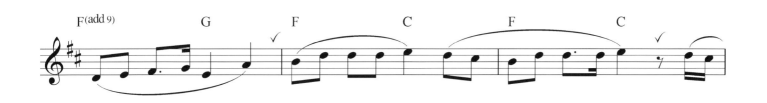

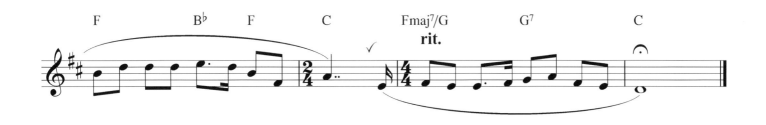

Willkommen
From 'Cabaret'

Words by Fred Ebb
Music by John Kander

You're The One That I Want

From 'Grease'

Words & Music by John Farrar

Angie

Words & Music by Mick Jagger & Keith Richards

Bridge Over Troubled Water

Words & Music by Paul Simon

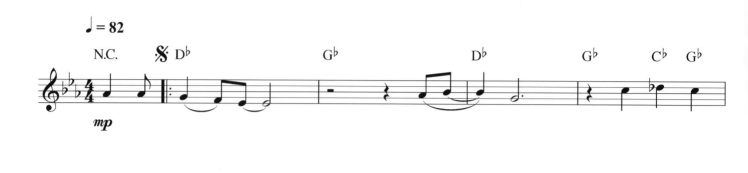

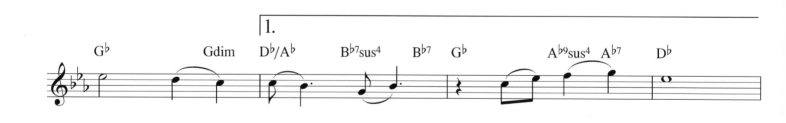

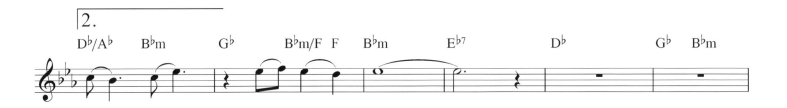

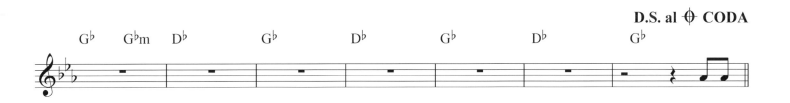

D.S. al ⊕ CODA

⊕ CODA

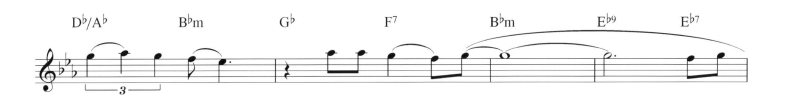

Can't Help Falling In Love

Words & Music by George David Weiss, Hugo Peretti & Luigi Creatore

(Sittin' On) The Dock Of The Bay

Words & Music by Steve Cropper & Otis Redding

I Got You (I Feel Good)

Words & Music by James Brown

The Lady In Red

Words & Music by Chris De Burgh

Unchained Melody

Words by Hy Zaret
Music by Alex North

91

What A Wonderful World

Words & Music by George Weiss & Bob Thiele

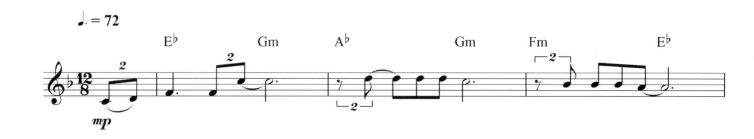

Stand By Me

Words & Music by Ben E. King, Jerry Leiber & Mike Stoller

Yesterday

Words & Music by John Lennon & Paul McCartney

Bringing you the words and the music

All the latest music in print... rock & pop plus jazz, blues, country, classical and the best in West End show scores.

- Books to match your favourite CDs.

- Book-and-CD titles with high quality backing tracks for you to play along to. Now you can play guitar or piano with your favourite artist... or simply sing along!

- Audition songbooks with CD backing tracks for both male and female singers for all those with stars in their eyes.

- Can't read music? No problem, you can still play all the hits with our wide range of chord songbooks.

- Check out our range of instrumental tutorial titles, taking you from novice to expert in no time at all!

- Musical show scores include *The Phantom Of The Opera*, *Les Misérables*, *Mamma Mia* and many more hit productions.

- DVD master classes featuring the techniques of top artists.